The Best of
Broadside

a humorous look at life in the Navy

By Jeff Bacon

Best wishes!

Jeff Bacon

Deep Water Publishing
Newport News, Virginia

Published by Deep Water Publishing
P.O. Box 12064
Newport News, VA 23612-2064

Cataloging in Publication Data
Bacon, Jeffrey Lewis, 1957-
    The best of Broadside: a humorous look at life in the Navy/
Jeff Bacon; foreword by John Lehman.
    p. cm.
    ISBN 1-881651-11-8
    1. United States. Navy—Sea life—Caricatures and cartoons. 2.
United States. Navy—Caricature and cartoons.   I. Title.
V736.B33 1992   759.1'0207
                        QB192-10743
Library of Congress Catalog Card Number: 92-72180

Quantity Discounts

Your club or organization may purchase this book in bulk at special discounts for fund-raising, premiums and sales promotions.
For details contact: Deep Water Publishing
                       P.O. Box 12064
                       Newport News, VA 23612-2064

Printed in the Unites States of America

10 9 8 7 6 5 4 3 2 1

Foreword

Life in the Navy, without a sense of humor would be impossible. The very life and death seriousness, the ever present physical danger and the unforgiving environment of the sea, develop in sailors an appreciation of the humorous side of life and an appreciation of its ironies. The best fighting ships are invariably also the happiest ships.

Jeff Bacon has helped to inject humor into the Navy life, and, as this fine collection of cartoons illustrates, has given expression to the ironies and occasional absurdities lived, observed or appreciated by sailors and marines of every rank throughout the fleet. Let us hope that this is the first of many volumes in this collection.

John Lehman

To Rebecca, the love of my life.

Thanks to the folks of Navy Times, to our families and buddies for all of their support, and to Howard Cohen and Craig Lilly for their editorial help. Finally, to the Sea Slugs—WBMN.

The wog's careful preparation earned him first place...and caused an uneasy stir among the crew.

The surface warrior forgot the first rule of survival
when visiting an aviation o'club.

Things we thought we would never see:
1) destruction of the Berlin Wall; 2) a peaceful transition of power in Nicaragua; 3) pilots posing as submariners to meet babes.

"Are you sure they said replenishment speed was 28 knots?"

Thanksgiving services in Deck Division

Beware the deadly barrel switch

Find the helo pilot in this picture.

Seaman Wright smokes his first and last cigarette
on the midwatch.

A slight translation problem during "leapfrog" exercises

When JAGs stand CDO

Popular bootcamp lore

Retiree hell

Supply Corps horror stories

P.A.O. war stories

Land stories

The old "testing the alarms gag" claims another victim.

Shipboard aerobics

When CO's play shortstop

If surface warriors had their own call signs

The day "Moonshade" tried to crash a SEAL/UDT head shaving party

A common scene two weeks before fitness reports
are due

Off duty metamorphosis

The guy from "An Officer and a Gentleman" after he got to flight school

Last day of the month, one short of quota. Things get ugly.

"Awright! Cookies!"

Surface warrior identity crisis

Hell week at the dreaded P.A.O. indoctrination school

When liberty call and pay day don't coincide

Submarine bullies

It looked like another long night for the "Fighting Nukes from Orlando".

Lt. Venglar tripped and fell on his sword, thus dooming himself to a lifetime of ridicule.

Man overboard drills are designed to: (1) Train junior officers how to maneuver the ship to facilitate rescue. (2) Train everyone else to never set foot outside the skin of the ship.

Barbershop diplomacy

Ill advised April Fool's Day joke

Yeah, right.

The phantom "klunk" common to most Navy schools

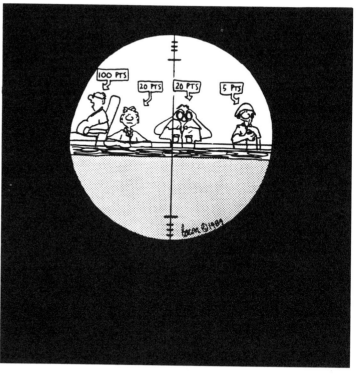

Standby for shot lines forward.

Swapping sea stories at the submariner officers'
club

"Chem-light" pranksters

"Group Think"

Late at night in flight deck control

When Cryptos shop for homes

Witty repartee at the USMC officers' club

The advantage of inflated fitness reports

When Admirals tell jokes

Navy recruits in liberty uniform

"Big John" went through his entire enlistment never knowing he had a hygiene problem.

Something you will never see

A common problem when LAMPS DETS embark

J.O. file management

On a 98-degree day in the Indian ocean, MS3 Howe pulls out the snowball he hid away 28,000 miles ago.

Anchor watch in San Diego harbor

Surface warrior equivalent of "carrier landings"

American sailors enjoying the local Hong Kong cuisine

What you don't want to hear the day after the captain's party

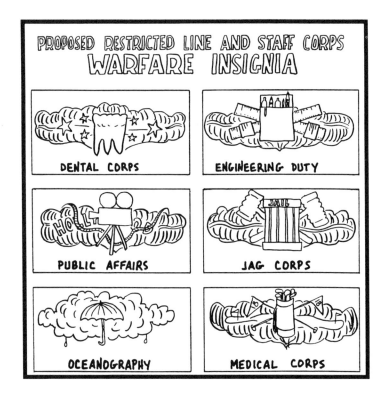

The X.O. never found his binoculars... although a diver did several years later.

THE CHILDREN OF THE USS NIMITZ BEGIN THEIR EASTER EGG WALKDOWN.

After two hours of trying to remember which to salute first -- the OOD or the flag, Ensign Sampson began contemplating a hotel room.

A matter of scruples

Before blowing tubes: (1) Know where the wind is.
(2) Know where the captain is.

The reason baseball never caught on as a popular flight deck sport

*hair standing on end

I.F.R: I Follow Roads

Navy coffee: The *REAL* adventure

General Quarters at the Defense Mapping Agency office

Unwittingly, Lt. Streed played an integral role in the development of satellite navigation.

Find the engineer in this picture.

What department heads don't see

The "tacking on" ceremony: no gain, no pain.

Another hazard of chewing tobacco

How detailers have fun

BUPERS phone tag

"Let me get this straight. They put us inside these solid steel vehicles that weigh, oh . . . say 50 tons. Then we drive them off a perfectly good ship into a hundred fathoms of water. We miraculously bob to the top and drive safely to shore. You go first."

CO standing orders: Notify CO of all C.P.A.'s less than five miles. OOD Supplement: Especially when passing on the same side as captain's cabin.

"Animal Night" at the surface warfare officers' club.

Seaman Dunlevy was never heard from again.

"When he gets out of the water, tell him next time not to salute until he gets aboard."

On slow days, the captain liked to have SA Sampson give the 1200 reports.

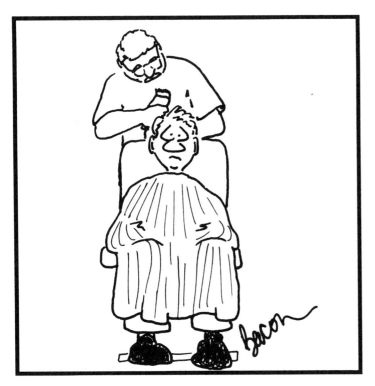

"Whoa! That was a big roll."

Mail Call. Indian Ocean. Insurance check.
Renewed doubts about lending his car to his
girlfriend.

Neither of these guys has ever had a date.

The first day of tropical attire is always the hardest.

This is why surface warriors shouldn't swoop their hair.

Young submariners learn quickly to heed all signs.

Much too small.

Safety mishap bulletin: SA injured by unidentified airborne object resembling Navy boondocker.

With horror, the submariner realized he was in the wrong officers' club.

In an attempt to change its image, the Supply Corps considers new slogans.

Jane Fonda film festival at the base theater

How to make a deck officer's day

Embarrassing camouflage faux pas

The Officer of the Deck from hell

MSSA Landers held the record for the shortest time
as a wardroom mess cook.

"Where the *@!#! have you been? We've been
looking all over for you."

"I don't like the looks of this . . . They just brought
on enough beer for six cans per sailor."

"Before you say anything else, you might like to know the captain is on the bridge."

"Hey! Keep your head down! They're gonna fire the shot line any second now!"

. . . then suddenly, the styling mousse gave out.

"300 total points, but I couldn't touch my toes."

Ensign Dickerson sees the moon rise at sea for the first time.

The P-3 crew begins its pre-deployment checklist.

The dreaded "post-shore-duty-amnesia".

"I can't wait to see Dickerson's face when they pull that 'sea bat' stunt on him . . . So when is this mail buoy supposed to come by anyway?"

He just keeps talking and talking and talking....

The flight aptitude rating exam: Where aviators first learn to talk with their hands.

"Big Eyes Liberty" in the Persian Gulf

"OK Captain . . . Let's see . . . We've been under for three days . . . at 12 knots . . . We're right here. . . . Whoa! Wrong chart."

"It's called *sunlight,* Cheng. They get it every day up here."

"Get ahold of yourself, John. . . we haven't left the pier yet."

"I don't think my wife understands the concept of frocking yet."

"What are you so worried about? This is only a rehearsal!"

"*My* umbrella? Oh, No . . . this isn't *my* umbrella. I, uh . . . bought it for my *wife*. Oh, but / wouldn't ever use it. Nope! No umbrella for me, nosiree!"

"Uh oh. . . looks like we have another one of those lateral-transfer meteorologists."

The joy of self moves

Watch relief in the Strait of Malacca

How you know the transition from civilian to military life is complete

Time management at its best

"Combat, bridge . . . Let's check that firing solution again . . ."

To the nukes, he was known affectionately as "Mr. Pep". To everyone else, unfortunately, he was simply a dweeb.

The old "shoe polish on the periscope" trick

The Navy Fashion Control Center

The harsh reality of the full length photo

How aviators view surface warfare